CHRISTMAS MAGIC

CHRISTMAS MAGIC

A Treasury of Christmas Memories

Dora D. Flack

Bookcraft
Salt Lake City, Utah

Library of Congress Catalog Card Number: 77-81884
ISBN 0-88494-322-4

5 6 7 8 9 10   89 88 87 86 85 84

Lithographed in the United States of America
PUBLISHERS PRESS
Salt Lake City, Utah

CONTENTS

Preface vii

Introduction ix

Butch Cassidy's Christmas 1

Reluctant Receiver 4

The Connivers 11

Tom Carlin's Christmas Miracle 16

Christmas Reward 22

The Family Santa That Came by Bus 27

Christmas Turnaround 33

The Skinny Snowman 37

Scout Sub 39

There Is a Way 45

Carma's Christmas 51

Chocolate and Vanilla 56

Round-robin Christmas 62

Gift Exchange 65

Unexpected Contribution 68

PREFACE

Christmas is . . .

Reading stories, especially St. Luke, around a glowing fireside;
Gazing at a tinseled tree with twinkling lights;
Rereading cheery Christmas cards from friends afar;
Shopping and spending too much for one you love;
Giving a gift anonymously;
Baking and sharing tasty goodies;
Worshipping at candlelight services;
Singing in the cantata;
Anticipating Santa's arrival.

   The stories within these covers are all that — and more. They could have a special meaning for you because they are all true, some related accurately to the most minute detail, even to the conversations; others have been changed slightly in order to recapture for the reader the emotion and insight of the events. Perhaps you can see yourself in them.

INTRODUCTION

In the *Deseret News* of Wednesday, January 5, 1977, in the section "Letters from Our Readers," appeared the following item addressed to the editor:

"Do you have room for one more Christmas story?

"I caught the real spirit of Christmas this year at the Foothill Station Post Office in mid-December. In that hectic, overcrowded lobby, a concern for total strangers by total strangers was displayed a dozen times during my hour's wait. Christmas chemistry was working like magic. And everyone felt it.

"An elderly woman, obviously not well, was leaning against the wall waiting for someone who was mailing a package. A man at the end of the line stepped out, improvised a comfortable seat from a sturdy ashtray stand and a telephone book. The woman sank to her perch, nodding gratefully.

"A two-year-old was crying as he was being held by his distraught mother. One grandmotherly woman found a box of crackers in her shopping bag. Another woman found a key ring, much to the delight of the child.

"A well-dressed but exhausted-looking man staggered under the load of about fifteen packages. He piled them on the floor with the help of those standing near him. It was a community effort to move the piles along the floor as the line moved forward. There were more hands than were needed to lift the boxes to the counter when his turn came.

"An Oriental teenager came in and before long was telling the woman next to him that this was his first Christmas and how excited he was about it. Everyone within earshot wanted to know more and shouted questions and greetings to him.

"A woman with arms full of bundles set her young daughter on the desk so the waiting would be easier for both of them. Not a person passed the little girl without a tickle, a question, a comment, or a candy bar. The little girl glowed from all the attention.

"A woman, stooped with age, got to the window and found she needed more staples in her mailing folder. An accommodating employee brought her a stapler, saving her a trip back home.

"A tough-looking guy in the typical leather jacket stood at the door, watching the room full of people chattering and laughing. The men and women on the other side of the counter looked pleasant and calm. The guy said: 'This is something else. I live in New York and believe me, I've never seen anything like this!'

"As I concluded my business at the counter, Alma Kruger, one of the employees, smiled and sincerely said, 'Have a really good day.' I already had!"

Evalyn Bennett

BUTCH CASSIDY'S CHRISTMAS

Lula Parker Betenson tells the following story about her brother Butch Cassidy, whose real name was Robert LeRoy Parker, also known as George LeRoy Parker. She asked Bob (Butch Cassidy) about the time he played Santa Claus to a family.

"What story is that?" he asked.

Lula said that she wanted to hear about the time he was almost frozen to death. She had heard that story and wondered if it were true. Butch told this story:

"That was the closest I ever got to leaving this earth. I got caught in one of those terrible December blizzards. My clothes were frozen stiff, and I was lost — I mean lost! I'd bought a horse from a fellow the previous May, and he'd told me the horse had homing instincts. So I let the horse have his head. Without my knowing it, the horse headed home for the corral where he'd been raised. I was too cold to worry about anything. It was close to Christmas, and I grew drowsy and dreamy. Suddenly I could hear beautiful music — singing. It was like hearing Ma play the organ and all the kids singing Christmas carols. I was home again and everything was rosy. I wasn't cold any more. I hadn't been that happy since — I couldn't remember when.

"Then I was in agony. The pain in my extremities was excruciating, and it felt like nails were being pounded into my chest when I tried to breathe. First I was burning up, then my teeth were chattering, and I couldn't stop it. Through my fog I made out a man and woman and a little boy and girl standing around me, rubbing me with snow out of a tub nearby. I groaned in pain. Why didn't they let me go home to stay? I hurt in every inch of my body. Because of the pain in my chest, the man decided I had pneumonia, and he sat up all night putting hot aspen branches over my chest and under my arms. I'd never heard of a cure like that, but it sure worked. They had to cut one of my boots off my frozen foot.

"When I asked him how I'd wound up there, he told me that he'd heard his dogs barking during that terrible storm. When he went outside he found me almost frozen to death, slumped over a horse at the gate of his corral.

"He got me into the house, and I started to thaw out. When he went back to the corral, he discovered that the horse I was riding was really a horse that had been stolen from him the spring before, but he didn't tell me until the next morning.

" 'I'll have you know I bought that horse fair and square. I'll settle the score with that skunk as soon as I can get around,' I told him.

"In a few days I was up and around. I hunted up that skunk who had sold me a stolen horse; he didn't live far away. I demanded a horse in exchange for the stolen one. And then I told him that I also wanted a buckboard and a team to use for a few days.

"I'd learned that the Hancocks were real poor nesters. They'd been cheated by land speculators and were living in a two-room shack. But they'd shared with me the little they had. I knew there wouldn't be much Christmas at their house that year, so I went into town in the buckboard and bought warm clothes for the family. I bought a sweater for the lady to wear around the house because it was so cold and drafty. And I got plenty of food. Then I picked up all the other makings of a Christmas and headed back to the Hancocks'. Those little kids had been so cute. They'd climbed all over me and had about worn out my ears with their Christmas chatter. It had been like being home when the house was full of our little ones.

"Well, when I reached that shack again I was so busy unloading all that loot and was so excited with the fun of being Santa Claus that I hadn't noticed three horsemen ride up. Suddenly I looked up and saw a sheriff's badge on the coat of one of the riders. My heart sank, but I went right on unloading, figuring this was the end of the road for me. Well, at least I was having a good time, and I was doing something worthwhile for a change. I couldn't help thinking how much better it would have been if the Hancocks had let me freeze to death rather than go to prison again. But then they'd never have had a Christmas if I had died.

"The Hancocks stood there as puzzled as anything; then Mrs. Hancock hurried and hid the kids' presents.

"When I finished unloading, I straightened up and said: 'Well, I guess this is it. Suppose I should thank you, Hancock, for saving my life, but I don't rightly know what for. Maybe it was to spread a little Christmas cheer — the real Christmas cheer.'

"The sheriff scratched his head and said knowingly: 'I've got a warrant here for George LeRoy Parker. Seen him around?'

" 'Sure,' I grinned. 'He was camping not far from here just a few days ago.'

" 'If you see him around, tell 'im I'm lookin' fer 'im.' The sheriff tipped his hat, smiled and winked, and rode off. 'Merry Christmas. Come on, boys, we'd better be on our way.'

"And that's as close as I ever got to being thrown in jail again."

This story is quoted from the book Butch Cassidy, My Brother, *by Lula Parker Betenson as told to Dora Flack.*

RELUCTANT
RECEIVER

Ethel slammed the telephone back onto its cradle.

"Now why did I let her wear me down?" she exploded. "Why should I be the object so that Primary class can learn about giving?"

She walked slowly through her silent home, counting her material blessings and enjoying the warmth and beauty of each room. Perhaps she'd been wrong in failing to put out her Christmas decorations.

Soft rays from the lamp lighted John's portrait on the glass table. He seemed to smile at her. She spoke to him as if he were sitting right there in his easy chair.

"You've left me with every comfort I need, not loaded with luxuries, but I'll never be a *poor* widow. Yet that's the way I'm being treated. Everybody's got to be good to the poor widows in the Church at Christmas."

Tears blurred John's likeness in the frame. "It isn't Christmas without you, John. Yet I wouldn't have you suffering again. I haven't the heart to put up a tree. Oh, our Johnny and the grand-children are thoughtful, but they're so busy with their own church projects and parties. Too bad the other children live so far away."

Since John's death less than a month ago Ethel had frequently found herself carrying on these lengthy one-sided conversations. His presence seemed closer then. But if anyone eavesdropped, they'd be certain she was senile.

"John, you'll never know how I felt last night. All those young couples came to carol — beautiful and happy, enjoying their togetherness. Nothing else has driven home so hard the fact that I'm all alone. I didn't sleep a wink after they left — couldn't stop crying. After they left I turned off the lights so no one would know I was here. You're ashamed of me, aren't you, John?"

Ethel's soliloquy was interrupted by the sound of childish voices caroling hesitantly and ever so softly on the front porch. One hand straightened her hair. The other tried to smooth the puffiness under her eyes. Every step was an effort as she half stumbled to the door. Why couldn't children ring a doorbell once and then wait? Then she smiled; no doubt they liked the sound of her long, musical chime — sounds like Christmas chimes, she thought.

At her half-hearted welcome the dozen or so children of the Primary class jostled each other self-consciously into the living room. Their smiling teacher brought up the rear, carrying a box of groceries — the children's charity offerings! Heaven forbid! The children milled around the room and into the dining room as if looking for something. Why did children insist on exploring in a strange house? That was rude.

She made a lame effort at graciousness, chatting individually with the children whom she knew well — and loved. Yes, she did. Then Jason tugged at her hand. She looked down into his sad eyes set in his freckled face.

"What's the matter, Jason?" she asked.

"Mrs. Atkin, I can tell you're a poor old widow. I feel so sorry for you. You don't even have enough money to buy a Christmas tree."

Ethel gasped as if she had been tomahawked from behind. Why, they had been exploring, hoping to find her tree. Regaining her composure she said firmly: "Now Jason, I have plenty of money to buy a tree, but I don't feel like it this year, not since my husband died . . ." Her voice trailed off.

Their teacher broke the embarrassed silence. "Come on, children, we'll have to hurry to the next widow on our list."

Ethel cooperated with her prod and helped to shepherd the children to the door, hoping she could forestall another crying jag before the last one was gone. As the youthful voices drifted away on the early evening air, she grabbed the small grocery box and hurried to the kitchen. She grasped the items one at a time and slammed them on the table, venting her anger with ungrateful exclamations: "Canned sweet potatoes! Can't stand them. Brown sugar! Sugar's not on my diet. A *large* can of pork and beans — you'd think I had a big family." On she went through each item, like a grocery checker, to the last one.

"Every one of those little kids has robbed his mother's pantry. Here I am taking food out of the mouths of babes. Deliver me! I'm just a poor old widow," her voice rose, almost to an hysterical pitch, "that can't even buy a Christmas tree!"

Her arms shoved the groceries aside and her head fell to the table, her shoulders shaking convulsively. At last she sat up and wiped her eyes with the back of her hand. Resolutely she stomped down the steps to John's basement workshop where she found the two large boards which he had once used to cover the bedroom window until the broken glass could be replaced. Back upstairs, she fitted them into place until no ray of light could escape to the outside. Then she turned out the lights all over the house and closed the bedroom door. With an extra lamp she could finish those oil paintings she'd been struggling with. This would keep her from thinking about herself. During the evening the doorbell rang twice at intervals, but she refused to stir from her solitary "studio," knowing the caller would never suspect she was home.

"This is where I'll spend my evenings until Christmas is over," she said. "Nobody can find me. And the phone can ring off the wall all day too. I refuse to answer it."

On Christmas Eve she applied her makeup carefully to hide the dark circles before leaving to spend the evening with Johnny's family. "I look like an old witch. Now that would shock the children if I lighted on their roof on my broom to substitute for Santa in his sleigh!" She surprised herself by chuckling out loud at the mental picture. "Guess I'm not hopeless if I can still laugh, and I mustn't take sadness into their home."

The doorbell chimed. "Hmmm, didn't get out of here early enough," she mused. She opened the door to admit the bishop. How wonderful! She needed a visit from him.

"Merry Christmas, Sister Atkin! My, you've been hard to find at home," he greeted.

"Well, I've had a lot to do," she lied. "Do come in, Bishop."

"I almost gave up delivering your fruit basket before Christmas. It's the third time I've been here."

"Thank you," she muttered. Then she begged, "Won't you please sit down, Bishop?"

"Sorry, but I've got to get home for dinner and family night. What are you doing for Christmas?"

"I'm spending it with Johnny's family."

"That'll be nice. Merry Christmas, Merry Christmas!" And the storm door closed behind him.

"Serves you right, Ethel Atkin. Look how your self-centeredness inconvenienced that overworked bishop. You don't deserve a visit from him." Her eyes stung. She clenched her fists and squared her jaw. "Now, Ethel, Johnny's children mustn't see you with red eyes. Don't you dare start bawling again." She walked to the glass table. A shadow was cast across John's face in the room's half light.

"John, what am I to do? All those years I was president of the Relief Society I helped fix those fruit baskets for the poor widows. Never once did I ask myself if that's what they really wanted. Took it for granted — custom. Never once did I pray to know specific needs or whether we were hurting their pride or diminishing their feeling of independence. That custom started in the Dark Ages, long before Social Security and pensions."

She turned on the lamp by John's picture so it would be lighted to welcome her when she returned home. "Well, John, I promise to put on my 'smiley face,' and no one will know how I feel inside. This Christmas is almost behind me, but how will I face another without you? I'll have to find a way."

Then she stopped, studying the face she loved. The lamplight had chased away the half-shadow. "What are you trying to tell me?" She stood meditating, coat on, gloves and keys in hand. "You're right, Dear, absolutely right. I remember the year we subbed for Santa and the fun we had. Now that I'm the receiver I'd forgotten the joy others experience in trying to give. I've been so ungrateful, so reluctant to receive."

Her face lighted like a Christmas bulb. "Why couldn't I sub for Santa again instead of being a selfish old witch? It will take year-round involvement to find the right gifts for the right family for next year. And that will be good."

As an afterthought she hurried to the kitchen and picked up the basket of fruit. Her grandchildren could help her enjoy it. After putting it in the car, she returned and carried out the box of groceries from the Primary children. She'd been puzzled about what to do with them.

The magic eye automatically closed the garage door after she backed out. Yes, John had taken good care of her; she was spoiled and knew it. Driving to the end of her street, she slowed the car and glanced at the old Smith home which had long ago been divided into cheap apartments. Not very inviting, she mused. She noticed that the front apartment was lighted for a change. A Mrs. Ames had recently moved in there. Although she hardly knew her, Ethel wondered why she was home on Christmas Eve. She'd been told that the new neighbor had a son somewhere in town. Ethel drove on, then stopped and turned the car around.

"I must be crazy to intrude on a stranger on Christmas Eve," she said out loud. "I can't help wondering if she's alone."

Mrs. Ames answered the knock and peered cautiously into the darkness. "Yes?" her voice quavered.

"Excuse me, but I'm Mrs. Atkin, your neighbor up the block. I saw your light on . . ." Ethel stammered awkwardly.

"Do come in. May I call you 'Neighbor'?"

"Please do. But I'm not a very good neighbor," Ethel smiled.

"I really haven't got acquainted since I moved in here. I'm not home very much — and it's only temporary."

"I've heard you have a son somewhere in town, but I'm ashamed to admit I haven't made much of an effort. Since my husband's death I've been pretty much of a homebody," Ethel said. What a flimsy excuse, she admitted to herself.

"Oh, I'm sorry. Mine's been gone nearly five years now." She motioned to the worn sofa, then sat down beside Ethel. Half smiling she patted Ethel's hand. "Might as well warn you. You never get used to widowhood."

"But why are you here alone tonight?"

"My son's family has the flu — not a very happy Christmas for them. I stay there a lot with my grandchildren so my daughter-in-law can spend more time at the hospital. But she wouldn't let me stay tonight for fear I'd get the bug too. I feel badly for Roger; he'll be alone too."

"Oh? What's the matter with your son?"

"Had a head-on collision with a drunken driver six months ago. He may never walk again. We hope this last operation will help some, but it's too early to tell yet. It's a gamble."

"Oh, I'm sorry." How lame and empty her remark sounded!

"That's why we all moved here, so we could be close to the hospital and so I could help out with the children. They're terribly cramped in their little apartment, so I do the best I can here. I'm close enough to walk over there."

"Why, I could drive you. I could take you to the hospital right now if you'd like," Ethel offered.

"No, no. Roger would be upset if I went out after dark. I don't see too well and he doesn't want me to stumble and break a leg. We can do without two of us laid up." Ethel felt her neighbor was making a valiant effort to be good-natured. As she studied her face she could see that her eyes did appear somewhat clouded.

"Cataracts," Mrs. Ames said, reading Ethel's mind. "But I'm so glad you stopped by. I know St. Luke almost by heart, but I'd be much obliged if you'd take the time to read the Christmas story, and could we sing some carols — just the two of us?"

Ethel looked around the room and spotted the leather-bound volume on the table. But her sharp eyes also observed the apparent humble circumstances of Mrs. Ames.

"Before I read, let me go to the car a moment," Ethel said. She made two trips, bringing in the fruit basket and the box of groceries. "Could you possibly use these?"

Mrs. Ames' face lighted. "My, my, I haven't seen that much fruit in a long time. My Social Security check doesn't go very far after rent is paid."

After reading and singing with her new-found neighbor, Ethel pulled the car door shut and started the motor. What a blind fool I've been, she thought, so steeped in self-pity that I couldn't see to the end of the block and know someone needed me! So fruit baskets are from the Dark Ages, are they? I guess Social Security alone doesn't eliminate need.

Then she smiled and spoke out loud. "Well, John, I thought I'd have to wait another year to sub for Santa. Her grandchildren are near the ages of ours. Do you think our grandchildren would like to share their Christmas? My, she must have had this son late in life to have such young ones. They're not members of the Church, so they can use my personal attention. Why, this world is full of people who need understanding if I'd open my eyes."

Ethel pulled her car to the curb in front of the florist shop, happy to see they were still open.

"This one will be just fine," she told the florist. "I'll take it with me, thanks." Surely she would be able to get to the hospital, visit with Roger Ames, and still get to Johnny's without delaying dinner.

With a genuine smile on her face she turned the key in the ignition. "Well, John, you needn't be ashamed of me anymore. I've learned to give and to receive."

THE CONNIVERS

Mark and his three brothers, Brad, Craig and Blair, were far from the ideal little boys awaiting Christmas. Even the Santa Claus threat didn't improve their behavior — much.

Every Christmas morning they tried, on the hour and halfway in between, to get their parents up: 1:30, 2:00, 2:30, and on up to six o'clock. But it never worked.

"Go back to bed. It's too early," their father always mumbled.

The suspense heightened each year until it was more than they could bear. "Mom, couldn't we open just one present before we go to bed?" Mark pleaded two weeks before Christmas.

A few days before Christmas Mark had worn down his mother's resistance to acquiescence. "Only one present now," she warned. "And that's final!"

That was all Mark needed. He cornered Brad who was just younger than himself. "Brad, have you got your present for me yet?"

Brad shook his head.

"Okay, you get me a flashlight. That's the one present I'll open Christmas Eve and we'll have this getting-up-early business licked."

"I don't get it," Brad scratched his head.

"Never mind, Dummy," Mark said, disgusted.

On Christmas Eve the four little boys each opened a gift, and Brad made sure that Mark got his flashlight. Mark and Brad shared the same bedroom. They slept fitfully. From their parents' bedroom the two could hear their father snoring. They knew Craig and Blair were also sleeping soundly. Grinning, Mark flashed the beam of his flashlight all around the room.

Brad asked: "Tell me now. Why is the flashlight so important?"

"Dummy. Where's your brain? I'm s'prised you haven't caught on. I thought you were smarter than that." He picked up the clock on their dresser and turned it up to 5:45. "You know Dad never lets us get up until 6:00. In fifteen minutes I think we can turn all the clocks in the house ahead. They'll all be six o'clock at the same time. Then Dad can't argue and say it's too early. That's why I needed the flashlight — so we won't have to turn on any lights. Gosh, I'm starved."

"Me too!" Brad said.

They tiptoed into their parents' bedroom. The rhythmic snores assured them that Dad was in a deep sleep. Mark flashed the beam on the dresser where Dad always put his wristwatch at night. It wasn't there! Then his mind clicked, but he didn't dare whisper his explanation to Brad. On Christmas Eve Dad always kept it on his wrist so he could look at it every time one of the boys bugged him to get up. The beam from the flashlight revealed that his arm was resting on top of the blankets instead of under them. How lucky could they be? Brad held the flashlight so Mark could use both hands to cautiously turn the watch to 5:50.

The boys continued their clock rounds from bedrooms to living room until all the clocks read 6:00 straight up. Mark flashed his light under the tree.

"Hey, Brad, we both got skiis," Mark checked the nametags with his flashlight.

"And look at these neat parkas! One for each of us," Brad whispered excitedly.

"Here's the sled Blair wanted," Mark said.

"Come on, Mark. Don't spoil all the surprises."

"Aw, we can always act surprised," Mark said.

Brad giggled. "Hey, Mark, I've got to admit it, you've got brains all right."

"You just don't appreciate me." Mark didn't crack a smile. "Okay, let's get the other kids first." They quietly awakened Craig and Blair.

The boys jerked up in bed as if pulled by puppet strings. "Is Santa here yet?" they asked, rubbing their eyes.

"I think so," Mark said, not admitting a thing even to the littlest boys. "Let's go wake up Dad."

All four boys burst into their parents' bedroom. "Hey, Dad! Can we get up?" they chorused.

Dad turned over in bed and mumbled: "Go back to bed. It's too early."

Mark put his fingers to his lips and shushed the impatient boys.

They stood quietly for a moment until they thought Dad had settled back into his sleep. Mother hadn't stirred. Mark held his little brothers, who were straining like dogs on a leash. Then he whispered, "Now!"

"Dad," they yelled. "Can we get up?"

"Go back to bed. It's too early," Dad grumbled again.

Mark whispered to his brothers, "He thinks he has to say that at least ten times before it's six o'clock." Then he spoke up. "But Dad, it *is* six o'clock."

"It is?" Dad opened one eye and looked at the luminous dials of his wristwatch. "I don't believe it. You're right. Mother, it's time to get up," he yawned.

"Can't be." She stretched an arm above the blankets and snuggled back down.

"But it is, Mom," Mark insisted. "Look at your clock on the lamp table. It's past six now. Come on, we gotta see what Santa Claus left. Aw, come on, Mom!"

Both parents, half awake, struggled into their robes and followed the boys down the hall to the living room.

From the living room Mark's voice echoed down the hall, "Hey, Mom, Santa Claus left the skiis!" He had to sound surprised so he wouldn't spoil things for his little brothers.

When the parents reached the living room pandemonium reigned as each excited boy dug for his coveted gifts.

"Break it up, you guys!" Dad ordered in a loud voice. "One at a time. You'll break something for sure. Man, that was the shortest night on record. I don't feel like I had even the usual broken Christmas Eve's sleep. How come those boys only disturbed us three times? They surely must have slept fast for a change."

After all the gifts were opened and the living room was a shambles of wrapping paper and ribbons, Mark and Brad were busily putting together the train for Craig.

Dad opened the drapes and turned on the Christmas lights outside. The tree lights shone brightly in the pitch blackness. "Say, I don't see any other lights on up the street. We're the first ones up. How come?"

"Guess they're all too tired," Mark said with a poker face, his eyes studying the train tracks.

"I can't imagine the Lloyd kids not being up as early as you guys," Dad puzzled. "Seems strange that not one other light on the street is on. We must have read the clocks wrong."

"Look at your watch, Dad," Mark urged.

"Says 6:30 all right. It agrees with the clock on the mantel."

"Well, I'm certainly not hungry," Mother said.

"Boy, I'm starved," Mark answered.

"Guess I'd better get some breakfast going before you kids get sick on candy." She went on out to the kitchen.

Mark caught his breath. "The jig's up," he whispered to Brad.

Mother swished back into the living room. "Back to bed — every one of you. Who did it?"

"Did what?" Mark asked, attempting innocence.

Mark jabbed Brad and kept his head down, as if studying the train track for a missing piece.

Mom continued. "It's funny that the kitchen clock says 3:00."

"Darnit! I forgot that one," Mark admitted.

"I'm going back to bed," Mother said, as she collected the Christmas socks filled with nuts and candy. "And I'm taking these. Not one mouthful! You can just wait for breakfast until I'm good and ready to get it. Go back to bed until six o'clock."

Mark Fitch, my nephew-in-law, is now the father of two carbon copies. He admits: "You know, more than opening presents on Christmas morning, I get a bigger kick out of telling those boys, 'It's too early. Go back to bed until six o'clock.'"

TOM CARLIN'S CHRISTMAS MIRACLE

My Christmas miracle happened many years ago in Richmond, Virginia, where I had played Santa Claus for about eight years. In fact, the particular year of my miracle I was awarded first prize as one of the ten best Santa Clauses in the United States.

In the department store where I sat on Santa's throne, the children filed up and were automatically photographed. As they left, their names and addresses were taken, whether they bought the picture or not.

One particular snowy afternoon about a week before Christmas business was light due to the near-blizzard outside. Suddenly a young, dirty-faced boy appeared in front of me, wearing shamefully ragged clothes and sneakers with the toes out. In a low, urgent voice he said: "Listen, Santy Claus, I'm bringin' my little sister up to see you, and I don't want you to promise her anything, because she's not gonna get it. There's no money at our house."

I agreed.

He left and in a few minutes came back with his little sister. Except for her dirty face and deplorable clothes, she would have looked like a beautiful blond angel. I picked her up and set her on my lap. The photographer snapped the picture. In my kindest tone I asked, "And what would you like?"

Well, she spieled off a list which included almost everything. You know, when you don't have anything, you want everything.

Coincidentally one of the store supervisors had come up behind Santa's throne and stood there listening.

As the little girl slipped from my lap, the attendant wrote down her name and address as usual. She took her brother's hand, and they hurried out of the store into the blowing snow.

The eavesdropping supervisor was practically in tears because of their pathetic condition. Immediately he spread the word all through the department store. Everyone caught the spirit, and by Christmas Eve every item on that little girl's wishlist was collected — all donations of the store employees.

I couldn't believe my eyes as I loaded my pack. Of course, Santa had a Snow Princess, who wore an exquisite ball gown, a thin stole, and pink ballet shoes. She wanted to accompany me on this very special delivery of toys and clothes. The store closed at 5:30. Outside it was snowing and was getting dark. We hailed a taxicab. I gave the black driver the address which we had obtained from the record of photos taken.

When we arrived at the address, we discovered that we were in the poorest section of Richmond — worse than a ghetto, really the dregs of poverty. We struggled out of the taxi with our load. Even the storm couldn't eliminate the stench of rotting garbage and stale boiled cabbage.

Our black taxi driver said: "Mista, ya'll might be Santy Claus, but I wouldn't dare stay in dis section o' town, dis time o' night fo' nobody. I'm not waitin' even fo' Santy Claus. No suh!"

"Well," I replied, "of course, I want to visit with this little girl." I was feeling uneasy myself. "I imagine we can find a phone — somewhere."

By this time it was totally dark and was snowing quite heavily. We walked up on the step of the rickety shanty and pounded on the door. Nothing happened. We pounded again — and again. That indescribable odor of poverty was overpowering here. The house was so old it was sort of tilted to one side. A couple of windows were broken. Again we pounded.

Finally the door opened. Inside, silhouetted against the dim light, was a wretched little woman with wild hair. She snarled, "Whatta you want?"

When Santa Claus and the Snow Princess arrive on a front porch on Christmas Eve, laden with brightly colored parcels, it's an occasion, but she was unimpressed. (I can't remember our little girl's name, so I'll call her Mary Lou Hill for expediency.) I asked, "Is this where the Hills live?"

"Naw! I threw 'em out," she said. "They didn't pay their rent." She griped on, then slammed the door in our faces.

By now the snow had developed into a good blizzard, and it was dark. What to do now? Ann, the poor Snow Princess, had soaking feet and was slowly freezing to death because she was still wearing only her light stole. I was dressed in my Santa suit and had no wrap to give her. After all, we really hadn't planned on being out in the weather.

There wasn't a street light anywhere in that part of town. I peered anxiously down the dark street. In the distance I could see a light. So we started trudging toward it, bending our bodies against the blowing snow. Suddenly a woman appeared out of the gloom. Instantly I asked her if she knew where the Hills lived.

"Why should I know?" she snapped back, and was swallowed up in the darkness. We kept moving toward the light. Suddenly I felt a tug on my arm. It was the same woman. She said: "I want to apologize. I do know the family. In fact, my name is Hill too, although they're not related to my husband. The father drinks and — well, they're not the happiest family in the world."

We stood chatting for a moment in the cold. She said: "I live right here. Why don't you come in and get warm, and I'll call my husband. Perhaps he'll have some information where they've moved to."

We stepped inside the small house. Surprisingly, it was spotlessly clean. She called her husband. While we waited, grateful for the warmth, she made us a cup of hot chocolate. Finally her husband arrived, but he didn't know of the whereabouts of Mary Lou's family.

"What's the light down the street?" I asked.

"It's a cafe-bar," he replied. "Somebody down there might have some information. You know, bartenders know everything."

This couple joined us out in the snow and went down to the bar with us. The small place was quite full — probably eight or ten people. When the four of us entered, me in my Santa Claus suit and my pack filled with packages, Ann in her soaked Snow Princess dress (she had now turned blue), and the Hills, we created quite a stir. We inquired about the evicted Hill family.

The bartender said: "Oh yes, I know of the family all right. Yes, I knew they were evicted, but I haven't got the slightest idea where they moved to."

I was puzzled and sick to know where to turn next.

A wizened old man made his way to my side and said: "I heard what you wuz talkin' about. Last week I saw that man drivin' a truck. Now lemme see. What wuz the name on that truck? I don't remember too good any more." He racked his brain for long moments, sort of mumbling to himself. His eyes suddenly lighted. "Got it! Hart's!" That's the name on the side of that truck. Hart's! (That is also a fictitious name.)

Hart's happened to be way on the other side of Richmond, down by the river in the warehouse district. It was getting late, and I was feeling desperate.

"Come on. We'll close the bar and help you find it," the bartender offered. Everyone pushed outside to their vehicles. There was a rickety old Ford, a pickup truck, and a big car — an ancient Chrysler, I believe. Everyone piled into their cars, and we started off across town to the Hart Company.

The snow was piling up in the streets. If it kept up this way, I might be stranded. Now whoever heard of Santa being stranded in the snow? At last we reached Hart's. We pounded on the gate of the high chain-link fence which surrounded the property. The night watchman appeared with his flashlight.

I explained our plight. He replied: "There's not much I can do for you. We hire quite a few part-time people. They'll work for a week — maybe two. I'm sure their records aren't kept. But let's go into the office and see what we can find."

Everyone piled out and crowded into the office where it was warmer than waiting in cold cars.

"Here's the personnel file," the night watchman said. He searched for a Hill card, but to no avail. "Let me call the man who owns this company. He's a fine gentleman and lives in Petersburg. I don't think he'd mind my disturbing him on Christmas Eve to help Santa Claus." He grinned.

Petersburg is a good twenty or twenty-five miles from Richmond, but the owner said he'd be right up. We waited about forty-five minutes. The roads were slick; traveling was hazardous. My time was running out. At last a sleek gray Cadillac drove up and the owner hurried into the crowded office. I explained our urgent situation.

"Let's go through the file," he suggested. After a thorough search, he shook his head. "Nothing here on any Hill."

As he closed the drawer, it stuck. He pulled it back and found that a sheet of paper had kept it from closing. Believe it or not, that paper was the personnel file of Mary Lou Hill's father, a file which should have been discarded, but somehow it had slipped under another card. The new address was on the paper.

By this time the owner had been caught up in our project and had telephoned his brother. He arrived with his wife and three children. Our entourage had increased. We all crowded into the waiting cars, five of them: the rickety old Ford, the pickup truck, the ancient Chrysler, the gray Cadillac, and a brand new Plymouth which belonged to the executive's brother. It was a strange caravan for Santa. The blizzard hadn't abated. Precariously we wove our way to the address on the personnel file.

Above the storm and the sound of the motor, chimes rang out occasionally. Richmond is known as the city of bells, and the sonorous sound calmed my agitation. Would we make it in time?

At last we arrived at the address. The home was one of those horrible little grungy dwellings, leaning sideways. Instead of window glass, they simply had put oiled paper in the opening to keep out the cold.

The Snow Princess was in a state of utter collapse. She hung onto my arm as we plodded through the deep snow up the path and onto the sagging porch. Everyone else piled out of the cars and huddled in a group. Their voices rose in unison in a spontaneous carol. At the precise moment Santa knocked on the door, it was Christmas morning — 12:00 midnight. The tongue of every bell in Richmond was released in one glorious melodic clangor.

The hair on my neck stiffened and the Snow Princess shuddered, not from cold, but from the thrill of that moment. We waited, our misty eyes glued to the door. At last, it opened wide, revealing a beaming Mary Lou. Her smiling face didn't register surprise — only confident expectation. She simply said, "Hi, Santa Claus, I knew you'd come."

Unless that now-grown girl, whose name I don't know, should happen to read this story, she'll never know the series of miracles that brought the Snow Princess and Santa Claus with a bulging pack to her door many years ago.

Tom Carlin is a popular radio host in Salt Lake City, Utah, and operates Theatre 138. Every year at Christmastime he relates this story on the radio.

CHRISTMAS REWARD

At the department store counter Iona opened her handbag to pay for the hose for her youngest daughter. The blood rushed to her head as she blurted out loud, "My billfold — it's gone!"

She rummaged thoroughly through the contents of her bag while the clerk waited impatiently. Confused, she said, "Oh, you go ahead and wait on someone else while I look through my packages."

Frantically she searched the two sacks she carried, hoping desperately that she might have dropped her billfold in one by mistake. But the sacks held only her purchases for her family. "How could I have lost it? Where?"

Mentally she retraced her steps from one store to another. Tears were crowding her eyes, and she blinked to keep them from spilling over.

Leaving the hose on the counter, physically she retraced her steps, searching counters and floors where she had shopped. Well, someone else is surely richer for my carelessness, she thought. It had taken her months to save that one hundred dollars for her shopping spree to the city. Her sewing profits were never large. How could she charge people what it was worth when they were also struggling? Even though the depression was supposed to be behind them, would they ever recover?

With her clever hands Iona was ingenious in making something elegant out of little. Fabric for new dresses for her three married daughters wouldn't cost too much, and a new dress would surely give their tired wardrobes a lift. John and Carol, still at home, had wishlists far too long. They would be cut to the bone now.

When she rejoined her patient husband, who had done his own private shopping, not a chiding word escaped his lips as he listened to her tale.

"Let's go to the newspaper office and place an ad," Jack suggested.

"It's a slim chance, but there might be some honest soul who found my billfold," she agreed. "They can call me collect. How stupid could I be? My name and address isn't even in it — no identification. Of course, that really wouldn't do any good. Almost anyone would keep a windfall like that. I'd spent only ten dollars. There was ninety dollars left."

Once the ad was placed, they headed for home. She didn't have any money left for more shopping. Sick at heart, Iona hardly spoke as Jack drove the forty miles. She was too busy silently scolding herself and scheming how she could use fabrics from the trunk where she kept her bargain buys. When one of her girls needed a new dress she didn't need to run to the store. Her store was in the trunk, full of fabrics purchased at half the regular price. But this year she had saved enough for extras — such big plans she had. The grandchildren would have to get clothes again, instead of toys, she reasoned.

Two days later the telephone rang. It was a collect call! A strange feminine voice asked, "Are you the one who lost your billfold?"

"Oh yes — yes! You found it?"

"How much did you have in it?" the voice inquired.

"Ninety dollars," Iona replied.

"Thank goodness. I was afraid someone might have taken part of the money before I picked it up off the counter. It's all here. Can you identify the billfold?"

"Of course. It's black imitation leather with a red lining."

"Oh, I'm so glad I've found the owner. There was no name or address, the voice wavered. "I've felt sick, knowing I had something that didn't belong to me. I live in Salt Lake. When can you come and get it?"

"Tomorrow is my husband's day off. I don't drive, but he can take me into the city then. That was my whole Christmas savings, and I've worked hard for it. Thank you, thank you!" She couldn't hold back the tears any longer.

The next day Jack pulled up in front of an old brick house on Third Avenue; it was the address given over the phone. The door was opened by a tiny girl, not more than five, Iona judged.

"Mommie, a lady's here," she called.

Iona could hear staccato footsteps across bare floors.

"Oh, do come in," she greeted cheerfully.

"I'm Mrs. Muir."

"I'll run and get your billfold out of my drawer. I've been uneasy with that much cash in the house."

While she was gone Iona's perceptive glance took in the spotless shabbiness of the interior — no floor coverings, makeshift furniture. A toddler peeked from behind a door and then inched into the room at Iona's warm smile. The child went directly into her welcoming arms. Iona noticed that both children wore faded, patched dresses — but they were clean.

The young mother was back in the room with the billfold in her outstretched hand.

"How can I ever thank you?" Iona asked. "Of course I want to give you a cash reward."

"Oh no, I couldn't accept anything — just for being honest. I didn't know how to find you. Then my neighbor happened to bring over the paper last night to show me some ads — Santa Claus, you know. I checked the ads to see if by chance anyone had advertised for a lost billfold."

Iona set the little girl on the floor and took out twenty dollars from her billfold. "Please take this — I'd feel better."

"No, no. Maybe . . ." her voice trailed off. "Bread cast . . ." She stopped abruptly, but kept smiling. "You can do your shopping now."

"But you need it," Iona caught herself. She didn't want to embarrass the young woman.

The woman's face reddened. "My husband has a job at last, and we'll have a payday the day before Christmas." The smile never faded.

Iona closed the door behind her and walked down the rickety steps. But her mind was spinning. "I'll finish my shopping before we go back home," she said to her husband. "I'm so glad I have that trunk full of fabric and trim. I can use that pink flocked nylon and make those two little girls look-alike dresses like they've never seen before. I'm sure they're perfect sizes three and five. I can just see their big eyes when they open my creations. Oh Jack, you should have gone in with me. That young mother makes me ashamed. She's pleasant, yet they haven't a thing. She must surely have been tempted to keep my money. I wish she had — I really do. She needs it far worse than we do. Her husband has been out of work. But she couldn't keep something that wasn't hers. What did she say? Bread cast . . ."

Two days before Christmas Jack drove Iona back into the city. He insisted on waiting in the car — his shyness often kept him from sharing special moments. Snow glistened on the trees and crunched underfoot as Iona walked up the sidewalk and onto the rickety steps. She rang the doorbell. In her hand she carried her frilly creations on child-size hangers protected with a paper sack. Under her arm she hugged a big box of baked goodies.

The same little five-year-old answered the door. "Mommie, that lady's here again," she called.

The young mother's staccato footsteps hurried from the kitchen. "Oh, Mrs. Muir. Now you haven't lost your billfold again, have you?" she laughed.

"No — no trouble this time. I'm just returning some bread cast upon water," Iona said. She handed her the box of goodies.

"And I couldn't resist," she said as she uncovered the frilly frocks. "Your little girls are adorable, and I have to see them in these dresses I made, to make sure they fit, you know." But in reality, she admitted to herself, she had to collect her own reward by seeing their reactions.

With trembling fingers the mother finally buttoned the delicate pink flounced dresses on her two cherubs. The pink set off their shiny dark hair and fair skin.

"A perfect fit," Iona pronounced with satisfaction. "I seldom miss."

"Whee! I'm a dancer!" The five-year-old whirled across the bare floorboards like a ballerina, the bouffant skirt bouncing. The three-year-old clumsily followed her.

"P'etty, p'etty!" the toddler chirped, trying to stand on tiptoes.

"They look like angels," the mother said, her eyes brimming with tears. "How did you know they didn't have a decent thing for church. Oh, thank you!"

I seldom miss all right, Iona thought. "Merry Christmas!" she said aloud.

Their excited thanks followed her down the rickety steps. Being careful not to slip on the snow, she thought: "I'm glad I lost that billfold. This has been more fun than doing for my own, and I'll manage to get their sewing done too, even if I have to sew the whole night before Christmas."

This experience happened to my own mother many years ago. She was a professional dressmaker and, like the proverbial shoemaker, was always so busy sewing for everyone else that she stayed up most of every Christmas Eve finishing lovely gifts for her own family.

THE FAMILY SANTA
THAT CAME BY BUS

My cousin Dick and his wife, Dorothy, were giving my husband and me a tour of the devastation left by the Teton Dam break June 5, 1976. Dick said: "Elinor is still having the hardest time of the whole family, even though the flood is four months behind us. Elinor and Ron lost their big two-story home as well as a small rental house. With their seven kids they're living in two HUD trailers out on their property."

Dorothy added: "It's close quarters for such a big family. When the warning came to clear out they were able to put quite a few of their possessions upstairs. Their home wasn't swept away — it just has to be bulldozed because of extensive damage."

"Look, over there is an example of what happened." Dick pointed to a lone green two-story house. We were in Wilford, the town which had been completely leveled by seventeen miles of stored water — mixed with rock, mud, gravel, and trees — boiling through the canyon below the now-fractured dam.

"Where's the town?" I asked.

"Gone — completely wiped out! That house is almost the only one left in town. This all used to be fertile farms and dairies, homes and barns. Now it's a gravel bed. This *was* a town. Now I'm not sure I can even show you where the big church was; no landmarks are left."

28 ~ *Christmas Magic*

"You're wrong, Dick," Dorothy laughed. "Remember that row of painted wagon wheels next door to the church? They weren't even toppled. Incredible!"

"How come this green house is still standing?" I asked.

"Go inside and you'll see." Dick walked down the lane to assure the owner, who was working on a fence, that we weren't vandals.

Huge numbers scribbled in red on the front of the house were stark evidence that it would be bulldozed. The front porch had been ripped off by the floodwaters and was nowhere in sight. We climbed up and over the threshold. The windows were gone. Watermarks could be seen just short of the ten-foot ceilings. Falling wall plaster revealed debris caked on exposed latheboards. Broken sections and door frames revealed the basic log structure, the reason why it still stood — a mute witness to its original sturdy construction before the turn of the century. The front of the piano had been removed, and manure and twigs mixed with mud hung like moss from all the strings. The keys were as rigid as rock. Yet a low, built-in cupboard in the living room miraculously held china, still stacked and unbroken.

Some of the kitchen drawers had rolled open. In one drawer a roll of masking tape was tipped rakishly at an angle, as if guarding the mud-coated valuables underneath, including a man's watch. The electric clock above the sink had stopped at 12:55 P.M. At the kitchen windows white and green nylon curtains fluttered like ghosts in the breeze. It was amazing that the torrent had not torn them down. One closet door stood open. Inside the closet, dried powder caked the top shelf. A lone, long dress, which appeared to have been a Bicentennial costume, hung from a hanger, mud-starched. A familiar monkey doll, lovingly handmade from a stocking, sprawled under a drawer, but the color of the doll was now undistinguishable.

We looked out the gaping windows and across the flat landscape to where at least a dozen new homes and barns were already occupied or in the process of construction. Heavy equipment was working the land. The whole area was a beehive of building activity — from Teton down through Sugar City and Salem and on through Rexburg, the swathe where devastation had been virtually complete.

"Dick, how can you take it?" my husband asked. "Gary and Jane's home in Sugar City and their hog farm were completely washed away. Your home was filled to the first floor and your whole thousand-acre farm is a gravel bed. Jared's two businesses were leveled. Elinor's house is gone!"

These three brothers, one sister, and their families had sustained almost total losses. Only Jared's home, on the hill behind Ricks College, stood untouched.

"Well, as I said before, it's been the hardest on Elinor," Dick said.

"Why?" I asked.

"The rest of us have been able to get away for at least a weekend. But Elinor has stayed right here, taking care of her kids and worrying over what's been ruined. She has been surrounded by this depressing devastation without a break. She doesn't realize that the rest of the world is still intact." Dick shook his head sadly.

Dorothy picked up the thread. "Gary and Jane's new baby was only a week old when the flood hit. Jane took all five of their little ones and went to Salt Lake City to stay with her sister for a few days. She was able to regain her strength. She knows this isn't the end of the world."

"But Elinor keeps looking back," Dick continued. "We can work at picking up the pieces. We can look ahead. As soon as we get our government settlements we'll rebuild. In the meantime we're working as hard as we can."

"How will you ever get your farm back in productive shape?" my husband asked, remembering Dick's gravel beds.

"Don't rightly know yet. But we'll make it."

"We've had so much help," Dorothy remarked.

"Dorothy's right. We were still slipping around in our mud, not knowing which way to turn. Almost everyone was in the same boat — only you can't navigate a boat in solid mud," he laughed. "Then busloads of people — men, women and young people — all organized through the Church, started to come from Utah, Montana, other parts of Idaho, and even from California. They brought their own tools, their own food, and food for us. They paid their own transportation and took time off work — just to help us."

"I know. We were scheduled to come and were upset when we were cancelled in favor of electricians," I said.

"Well, when all those thousands of people started to come we had to tell them what to do. Their vigorous hands gave us more than help — they gave us courage and hope. They could accomplish in one day what it would have taken us weeks and months to do. It made the whole difference," Dick said. "I used to get so mad at those Utah hunters who came up here and hunted on my property. I'll never cuss a Utah hunter again."

Dorothy added: "All the denominations in the area banded together with the Red Cross and the Salvation Army. The LDS Church sent truckloads of supplies as soon as they heard that it even looked like the dam would break. Relief supplies were pouring in immediately."

I commented, "Thank goodness it happened during the day and during summer school, so most of the Ricks College dorms were empty."

"They weren't empty long," Dorothy said. "Hundreds lived there until other apartments and trailers were cleaned up and ready for use. And that Ricks College cafeteria — they served over two hundred thousand meals without charge to the victims. Think of that!"

After leaving our cousins in Rexburg (jokingly spelled Wrecksburg), my husband and I wondered what we could best do to help them. It was October, and winters in Rexburg are very cold; the wind blows almost constantly, adding to the chill factor. We thought of all those people trying to keep warm in trailers. We thought of our closets at home, stuffed with warm clothes, and wondered how we would ever replace a lifetime of accumulation for living if it were suddenly swept away. We thought of the loss of their food storage. We thought of Christmas, not far off.

As soon as we arrived home, a couple of cousins and I organized a shower. We invited nearby relatives to come on the last Saturday in October to help tie quilts for and share their bounties with the flood victims. I had predetermined what was needed, according to size and sex and households.

Our relatives' generosity was overwhelming. Those from far away sent money. Some of our neighbors begged to join the effort. My husband's cousin Royal volunteered his bus — a school bus which he had converted into a luxurious home on wheels. Royal, his wife, my husband and I loaded the bus one Friday early in November and headed north for Rexburg.

Our cargo included many cases of home-bottled fruit and jam (which is always a labor of love), good clothes (some of them new), gorgeous tied flannel quilts, other new bedding and towels, kitchen utensils, pans and small appliances, books and *Boys' Life* magazines, games, plus yards and yards of fabrics for Christmas sewing so all could have smart *new* clothes that fit.

When we arrived only the adult couples were invited for the gathering of the clan at Dick's home in order to keep the gifts a secret from their children. As we unloaded, Dick exclaimed, "Why, it's like Christmas." The end of his spacious living room was filled.

Gary asked: "You mean our relatives did all this? Why, not very many of them even know us."

"That's right," I agreed. "But we're still kin — families."

"I can't believe that anyone would do all this, just for us," he said. "This is the real spirit of Christmas — early."

As we emptied boxes, his wife Jane shook her head, her eyes brimming with tears. "Believe me, we've surely seen Christianity in action in our trouble." Then her eyes lighted. "Oh, look at those darling navy-and-white shoes. They'll just fit my baby — he hasn't any shoes yet. And that baseball mit. Would you believe it? It even has T-o-d-d written on it. Won't my Todd be excited — it's like new, and it will just fit his little hand." The mit had been donated by another relative, also named Todd, yet he was unaware of the other Todd's existence.

Elinor pulled a cardboard box closer and squealed: "Oh, can I have the *Boys' Life* magazines? Let's divide these books age-wise to suit our kids."

"I have too much," Jane objected, as she encouraged others to take their first choices — yet she was the one with five children who had lost everything.

Dick was still thinking Christmas. "Say, Santa really came early this year."

Elinor picked up a luxurious purple bathmat set. It had been used slightly but looked brand new. She gently rubbed it against her cheek. No matter what their government settlement amounted to, it would mean a new home for their big family. She remained quiet and pensive for a long time in the hubbub, then during a lull, with the bathmat still pressed against her cheek, she said: "I've been planning my new bathroom around this. There's no more looking back."

Surprised and relieved, Gary spoke up. "Since when aren't we looking back, Elinor?"

"As of right now. We're only looking ahead. Now I know everything's going to be all right."

To hold back her own tears of relief at the change in Elinor, Jane said: "And we'll start sewing up a storm for Christmas. We've gone from plenty, to nothing, and now we're on the road back. Thanks to this unique family reunion, our kids will have a glorious Christmas. But they'll never know that this year Santa came by bus."

CHRISTMAS TURNAROUND

Sara watched her ten-year-old son, Jason, open the last of his stack of Christmas gifts — an Etch-a-Sketch. He flipped the knob and the line raced across the glass. "Neat," he yawned. He surveyed his loot: loads of flashy clothes, especially the sleeveless down-filled vest which had been at the top of his list, a Pong game, and other odds and ends. "Daddy, is this all?" he asked.

"Is this all?" Sara repeated incredulously. "Think of all the children in this country who would have been happy with just one of your gifts. Young man, there are children who don't have any, believe it or not. Think of the starving Chinese!"

"They don't celebrate Christmas." Jennifer, a high school junior, was blasé.

"Well, if they did . . ." Sara glanced around the room uneasily. Jason, Jeff and Jennifer each had a chair draped with clothes and stacked with luxuries. "Oh, you ungrateful kids!" She had searched hard for just the right sizes and colors, presents that each one had requested, and some they hadn't asked for. Christmas had cost a bundle. Blake would be in debt until July paying for it. She couldn't blink back her angry tears fast enough. Through the blur she relived their joyous Christmas Eve just last night, right there in that same living room which was now a shambles of boxes, wrapping paper, ribbons and scattered gifts.

On Christmas Eve Blake and the three children had stood around the organ, singing lustily while she breezed through one carol after another on the keyboard. What fun they'd had! The red coals in the fireplace gave the room a cozy, welcoming atmosphere. A special something was in the air. Was it Christmas chemistry? The huge cone and evergreen wreath above the mantel was Blake's creation. The house was an artistic masterpiece of Christmas ornamentation. The lightly flocked spruce, trimmed with red velvet bows and glittering gold ornaments, was exquisite enough for the White House. The children's eyes danced with anticipation as they eyed the gifts under the tree, all wrapped uniformly in gold paper and tied with red ribbon and bows — truly a Christmas picture for a *Better Homes and Gardens* spread.

"Can't we open just one present tonight?" Jason asked.

"Why not?" Blake responded.

Blake handed one package from under the tree to each member of the family. Sara's was a medium-sized square box from her mother and father. She felt it, searching for clues, then shook it and was even more puzzled.

"It rattles," she said. "I'm surprised it's so big. When I went shopping with Mother we were looking at watch pendants and I really thought that would be their gift to me. This box is quite heavy. It can't be a tiny watch." She laughed and her eyes sparkled in anticipation. "Don't you just love Christmas, kids?"

"Yes," they all echoed.

Each in turn opened one gift, and the whole family enjoyed the excitement together. At last it was Sara's turn.

"Open yours now, Mom," the children urged, sharing her expectation.

"I don't really want to. It's so much fun waiting," she said pensively. Again she squeezed the box and shook it. "What on earth can it be?"

"Open it and see," Blake prodded.

At last she slowly untied the shiny ribbon and carefully pulled the tape loose. Now she was down to the white box. Wishing to prolong the expectancy, she hesitated before removing the lid. "If it isn't the watch, what would they give me?" She lifted the lid. Inside was an assortment of colorful rocks!

Blake laughed loudly. " 'What on earth' is right? You can't get much closer to the earth than rocks."

Sara tumbled the rocks in the box absently, almost in a state of shock. "Well, I guess they're to put in our indoor rock garden."

"That's a funny gift," Blake said.

"Maybe the watch is under the rocks," Jennifer suggested.

Immediately Sara began fingering through the rocks, looking for a small jewelry box. "None here. Wait! Here's something." From the bottom of the box she drew forth an envelope and peeked inside. "A $50 greenback! Well, I guess I can buy my own pendant watch."

The Christmas Eve scene faded as Sara looked through the blur of her angry tears on Christmas morning.

"I hate Christmas!" she exploded.

"What?" Blake was stunned.

"I hate Christmas," she repeated. "We were so happy last night, singing and simply enjoying each other. This morning we've frantically unwrapped one present after another, nobody even stopping to see what anyone else has, not being grateful or gracious, expecting more, and more, and more! If I just had the one gift — the box of rocks — even if it hadn't had any money in it, I experienced more enjoyment out of guessing, feeling, and anticipating than I've known this morning."

"I think I know what you mean," Blake said slowly.

"It's all out of perspective," Sara went on. Now that she was wound up she decided to get it off her chest. "After all, whose birthday is it?" The family sat in a moment of stunned silence, allowing the idea to settle. Then Sara continued, "We don't honor the Savior when we give all these extravagant gifts."

"Gosh, Mom, how could we give gifts to Jesus? He isn't here."

"You're right, Jason," Blake spoke deliberately. "He isn't here, but when we serve our fellowmen in need, that's the way we give gifts to Jesus."

"Aren't we fellowmen — when we give to each other then?" Jeff asked.

"Yes, but we don't need all this," Jennifer said.

"If we had even gone and shared our voices with shut-ins," Sara said. "We'd have been really happy, and we'd have made someone else happy. We do sound pretty good, even if I say so myself."

"I don't know, Mom," Jennifer said. "You know when our trio from school went to sing at that rest home the other day? Well, we stayed and talked to some of those people. I was talking to one old lady and she said, 'I hate Christmas' — just like you said. It surprised me and I asked her why. She told me, 'Because all those do-gooders come and give us programs, just at Christmas. They ease their own conscience that way. They never do thoughtful things the rest of the year.' You know, I felt guilty too."

Sara broke the silence that followed Jennifer's comment. "I wonder if we can't change that. We think our individual efforts don't count for much, but they do. Why don't we work up some programs and once a month during the whole year we'll go and share our talents with shut-ins? Maybe we could make the Christmas chemistry a year-round feeling."

"And we could make goodies together to take with us!" Jennifer was excited already.

"I've got another suggestion," Jeff said. "Why don't we sub for Santa next year? I'd be willing to go without presents."

Jason ran to his room and returned with his fat piggy bank. He shook it and said: "It's almost empty because I spent my money for Christmas. But we can use this to start saving for a poor family."

"That would get us off the debt hook another year," Blake smiled.

"Would you all be satisfied next year with just one present each?" Sara asked.

"You mean we really would be fellowmen too?" Jason asked.

Sara laughed. "I think so. You know, on that first Christmas two thousand years ago God gave one gift to the whole world — his Son, our teacher and our Savior."

The bright Christmas sun spread its rays through the tall window and bathed the family in its glow.

THE SKINNY SNOWMAN

A heavy snowfall the Sunday before the holiday assured us of a white Christmas. Following the storm the air was crisp and clear. Peace and harmony pervaded the very atmosphere.

Returning from a last-minute cantata rehearsal at the church, I drove down the hill toward home. Two giant figures loomed in the middle of the street almost in front of our home. As I neared them I could distinguish the two tall neighbor boys putting the final touches on a twenty-foot-tall snowman. Mark, the younger brother who stands about six foot four inches tall, was straddling the shoulders of his older brother who is yet a mite taller. He was reaching to put a cap at a rakish angle on the head of the skinniest snowman I had ever seen. The boys moved to the side of the road as my car slowed.

With a mischievous grin on my face I steered straight for the snowman, as if to topple it. They raised their hands, half pleading, half threatening. Of course I swerved around it, sparing their creation. As I pulled into my own driveway, Mark was back up on Dave's shoulders, finishing the face.

Mr. Snowman's coal eyes looked down on every car that went up or down the street. Each car swerved to accommodate him.

When our family went back to church, he was still standing straight and skinny. I wondered how long he would last with Mark and Dave standing guard.

As we returned from church we expected to see Mr. Snowman reduced to a heap in the road. But from the top of the street we could see him still standing. Coming closer, we thought our eyes must surely be playing tricks. He had moved to the curb. How?

Upon inquiry we learned that a police car on its rounds had happened on the scene — or perhaps had been called by a neighbor. Mark and Dave were persuasive with the policeman. Or was it that special Christmas magic that was the convincing ingredient? On his radio the policeman had relayed a message, and in a few minutes a city snowplow had arrived. Ever so gently using the big blade the snowplow driver had nudged Mr. Snowman to the side of the road without collapsing him. There he stood until the Big Day, a reminder that Christmas magic creates a feeling of good will with public servants too.

SCOUT SUB

Since I was senior patrol leader I stood at the door of the old log Scout house. "Wipe your feet on that rug!" I warned as each boy entered. I looked down at my uniform. My trouser legs were almost mid-calf. My scout shirt sleeves hadn't met my wrists for ages, and the shirt was faded with age. I felt self-conscious in it, but I couldn't bug my parents for a new uniform now that I was almost ready for Exploring. If only I could finish those Eagle requirements.

I surveyed the big log room with pride. It was really great that our troop could hold meetings in a log cabin that was over seventy-five years old. Believe me, we took pride in keeping it up, too. Outside the wind and snow were blowing hard, but the cabin was snug. A crackling fire burned in the rock fireplace at one end of the big room.

At eight sharp I called the boys to attention for posting of the colors. Inspection and other preliminaries followed. We were lucky to have Joe and Meredith Palmer for our Scoutmasters. Joe was tall, and I guess you could call him down-right handsome. He was graying at the temples. His big voice boomed out occasionally over our hubbub. You can't very well have a Scout meeting without noise. The Scout quiet sign was raised several times and picked up by the boys so that troop business could be transacted.

After a fast game of "Around the Chair" to get rid of the wiggles, we plopped on the floor in front of the blackboard. The

Green Bar announced the next matter of business which included instructions and necessary preparations for an overnight winter camp. This was Meredith Palmer's department. After showing us actual examples of different kinds of packs, he told us a lot about the art of packing. He said: "Of course, you little guys can't pack much in your extra pair of pants. But mine . . ." We all roared. Meredith was several handspans across. "Why, I could pack everything in mine."

The lights were turned off and we made the rafters ring with song. You'd never believe how much real music Meredith could get out of us around a roaring fire when the wind howls outside.

I stayed behind after the other guys had gone. I was almost afraid to bring up my idea for a service project, which was the only thing keeping me from my Eagle. I sort of hung around, cleaning up, not knowing how to jump into the subject. Joe was gathering up papers at the table. He looked up and said, "Mark Severin, when are you ever going to move on your service project?" I was glad he broke the ice.

"That's exactly what I want to talk to you about," I said. Meredith sat down with Joe, and I sat on the floor, hugging my knees. "During the Thanksgiving weekend I talked it over with my family. I want to sub for Santa."

They glanced at each other. Meredith shook his head and waggled his finger at me. "You're too skinny, boy. I know, you really want me to stand in for you. Right?" He patted his ample middle.

I laughed. "I hadn't though of that."

"Too bad I don't have a Santa suit." Meredith slapped his knee.

"You'd make a neat Santa Claus at that — no padding necessary." I ducked my head because it was the truth, but I wasn't sure how he'd take it.

Their laughter almost shook the antlers of the deer head mounted on the crossbeams above. Then they were sober. "How do you propose to earn money for a thing like this? You're not loaded — we know that. Are you sure you haven't got a tiger by the tail?" Joe asked.

I gulped. "How did you know what I'd planned to do?" I asked.

"What do you mean?"

"Well, that 'tiger by the tail' bit, I had planned to rent the Disney film *The Tiger Walks*. Thought I could get permission to use the cultural hall in the church building. I figure this is a community project. You know, the townspeople would be helping by coming to the movie. Here's a sample of a ticket I've typed." It read:

The Tiger Walks
December 15
Suggested Contributions:
Adults 75¢   Children 35¢

I went on: "I'd sell popcorn and candy to make extra money. The proceeds would provide Christmas for a family. I figure I'd learn a lot in a service project of this kind."

"A whole lot!" Joe nodded. "But what happens if you don't have a good turnout for the movie and don't make much money?"

"Don't say that. It has to succeed. The troop could sell tickets and put up chairs and help sell popcorn and candy that night. It would make them a part of the project. In a way they'd be giving of themselves this Christmas."

"What about a prospective family?" Meredith asked.

"Mom called the South Davis Community Council for a family."

"You know this will take your own Christmas?" Joe warned.

"Sure. But it will be Christmas enough, if I can do a good job, that is. I never realized that there are people who wouldn't have any Christmas if someone didn't sub. Sounds fun to me."

Joe nodded. "We're behind you all the way, Mark. I think you've got a great idea."

The next two weeks were busy ones. Even in school I found myself worrying over all the details. What if people wouldn't come to the movie? It cost me $27.50 to rent the movie, and that would have to come out of the profit. I swallowed hard every time I thought of that little detail. Selling tickets was a pretty discouraging business. Everyone was too busy to listen. One Saturday I tramped from door to door for four long hours without selling one ticket. I learned one thing — I'm no salesman. But it was hard to smile and be enthusiastic without any encouragement. I felt like the smile was frozen on my face.

Grandma and Grandpa ran a small neighborhood bakery. They kept a jar on the counter by the cash register and explained my project to their customers. When the coins stacked up in the jar, Grandma exchanged them for green money, and it looked like the jar needed some help again. With my grandparents' help and advance ticket sales, I had enough to pay for the movie rental.

A local newspaper ran an article on my project and included some pictures. It made me feel important. At school I almost enjoyed the razzing of the kids: "Hi, Santa Claus!" "Good ole Sub!" It was great to be "neat."

The night of the movie was crisp and cold — a perfect night for everyone to be enjoying a crackling fire in the fireplace at home. Mom and my sisters Brenda, Karen, and Jeannette had popped and sacked corn to be sold. I was sick inside when I saw that mostly kids sauntered into the recreation hall. Tonight I had to earn enough for my Christmas family. But kids don't have much money, especially before Christmas, I thought. I'd probably carry home the popcorn and candy I intended to sell. Not many of my school buddies showed up. That really shafted me. I felt like hiding behind the velvet curtain on the stage. I'd go broke for sure and what would happen to my Christmas family? I was committed. But by the time the movie started there was a fair-sized audience, and they all bought.

That night, when I counted my haul, I had over seventy dollars' profit. What really surprised me was that later, at church, people occasionally shook my hand and left money in it — for my project, they said.

The agency assigned me a family consisting of a mother and her two children — a boy, four, and a girl, six. Mom went with me to get acquainted with them and to see what they needed. When Mrs. Smith answered the door I knew that something was wrong. She had such a puzzled look. She brushed her hand across her forehead and said: "But I thought only rich people did this. And they've sent a boy!" Jiminy Christmas! I was afraid she was going to cry.

Mom took over and said: "I'm sure we can provide a good Christmas for your children. What do they need?"

"Oh dear! Oh, we'll get along. We really don't need a thing."

Who did she think she was kidding? "Do you have Christmas tree ornaments?" I ventured. What a lame question!

"Oh, we don't need a thing," she insisted. Now how did she think we could do anything if we didn't know what to do?

Mom talked to her on the phone a few times, trying to wheedle information out of her, and learned that she was a very independent little woman. She'd recently been divorced; she'd had a heart attack and a stack of other troubles. She really needed a lift with Christmas, but she wouldn't say how. It was a good thing Mom was such a good shopper and knew what they might need — I think they call it woman's intuition, or something like that. And could she ever stretch my dollars when we went shopping!

At school I was given a tree for my family, but trimmings were expensive. A friend donated ornaments and icicles, and I bought the lights. Christmas was a hair away when Mom asked, "Mark, what do you want for Christmas?"

"Nothing at all," I said, and I meant it. "You've helped me so much. I never realized before how much time and money it takes to have things under a Christmas tree."

The day before Christmas I bought the turkey and all the trimmings for the Smiths' Christmas dinner. Mrs. Smith still wouldn't tell me what she needed. I had five dollars left, and

I decided to give her the money, along with a box of chocolates which I bought out of my own money. I delivered everything to the Smiths and dragged myself home. Christmas Eve I went to bed with such a gnawing feeling in my stomach that I was sure it was an ulcer. I hadn't done enough for them. I'd really goofed. Whatever made me think I could tackle a project like this in the first place? Would the little kids be happy?

On Christmas morning I was awake before anyone else, but not because I expected to find anything for myself. I just plain hadn't slept. But I knew I had to make the best of things. "Merry Christmas!" I shouted. My "ulcer" was gone and I did feel better. Under our own tree I found a Swinger camera with my name on it. Just what I wanted! Excitement ran high at our house, but my thoughts were with the Smiths.

Suddenly the telephone rang. I picked up the receiver and shouted, "Merry Christmas!"

"Santa?" Mrs. Smith asked, a catch in her voice. Jiminy Christmas! She sounded like she was going to cry.

"Yes?" I was so anxious I almost climbed through the phone. All I heard was silence! Now I knew I'd failed.

"I . . ." More silence. "I just want you to know that a boy has given us the most wonderful Christmas we've ever had."

"Whoopee!" I couldn't help it. But I could hear the kids clamoring to talk to Santa Claus. Hey, that was me! I couldn't believe how excited and happy they were. Jiminy Christmas! I caught myself wiping my eyes with the back of my hand. Why, this was the most fun of my whole life! I decided this was what Christmas was all about.

I had finished earning my Eagle in the process, but I had learned something else too. I learned why they also give a guy's mother an Eagle pin along with the Scout.

THERE IS A WAY

"Is there room for one more?" latecomer Capt. Jay Hess asked, as he picked his way around and over the rather boisterous group of officers seated on the floor of the officers club in Tahkli, Thailand. He had just changed from his sweat-stained flight suit after debriefing his flight. There had been lots of flak, some MIGs and SAMs — a very close call.

On the movie screen above the men flashed the title *There Is a Way*, the story of those men who flew F-105s over North Vietnam. Each pilot was to fly a hundred missions before returning to the States. Jay heard a faint voice behind him: "There ain't no way. We'll never make a hundred missions and live to tell it."

Jay's thirty-first mission was his waterloo, August 24, 1967. He had been captured and was a prisoner in Hanoi. Injuries, indoctrination, interrogations, torture, adjusting to prison life all added up to a seemingly endless nightmare.

The months dragged into December. Jay shared a dingy gray room with three other pilots: Mike McGrath, Gerry Gerndt and Konrad (Konnie) Trautman. Mike had gone down first, in June, and was the most seriously injured. Even by December he still supported his badly damaged shoulder and arm with a sling. He had tried to set it himself. Jay's arms and wrists were still weak from the "interrogation procedures."

Each man spent his burdensome hours in his own way. It was always too hot or too cold. By mid-November the coldest winter of their lives began. Jay spent much of his time walking around the room to keep warm and to build up his strength. He reminded himself of the lions he had seen pacing back and forth in a cage in the zoo back home.

The room was quite large with four pallets at one end. Boards had been fastened together for beds. A skimpy straw mat was a poor excuse for a mattress. Two thin blankets and a mosquito netting were rolled up at one end of the pallet during the day. At night the men spread one blanket over the straw mat and another over themselves, then froze all night. The netting was suspended from nails on the wall like an oblong tent over each person. During subsequent winters the prisoners fashioned their meager bedding into a sleeping bag with the netting between the thin blankets. They slept much warmer this way, since the netting acted as insulation.

Hordes of rats ate through the netting, especially during warmer weather, and nibbled on toes, although no one was seriously hurt by them. Dreams turned to rat nightmares.

The men were issued a toothbrush, a bar of soap, a towel, a tin cup, a spoon, a small teapot for water, a fan, and a small crude broom with a short handle, similar to a whisk broom. Prison garb was black pajamas. At first Mike's first pajamas had been very small, but as more aviators were captured the Vietnamese saw how large the men were in comparison to themselves, and they increased the size of the clothing to ridiculous proportions. Jay and Mike could almost get into the same outfit at the same time. The dyes were poor and the black faded to an ugly gray. In hot weather the men were issued faded wine-red and gray wide-striped trunks and short-sleeved tops. Their shoes resembled thongs, the soles fashioned from old rubber tires; inner-tube toe straps were fastened into small slits in the sole.

Everything was the same filthy gray — walls, floors, ceilings, window bars over the small windows. No color was present except the dull dark red in their summer clothing.

At 5:30 or 6:00 A.M. the gong awakened the men to another endless day. Scrambling from their pallets, they rolled up their bedding and netting, slipped into their thongs and listened for the turnkey to bang on the door. As the door opened the men were expected to be right there, bowing low, almost double, before their captors.

Once during the long day they were permitted to go outside their room to a small handkerchief-size courtyard to wash dishes at the tiny well, empty their slop pails, and sweep out their filthy quarters. They could never see anyone else, although they knew there were other captives through the wall. They could not communicate. Even in their own room they conversed only in whispers.

The men kept track of the passing days by memory and began to think of Christmas. But there was no use even talking about the Christmas spirit.

"There ain't no way," Jay said, recalling the statement of the other pilot that day at the officers' club in Tahkli. His thoughts traveled the thousands of miles to his home in Bountiful, Utah. He knew that his five children would be excited for Santa's visit in spite of his absence. He wondered how his wife was managing. Did she know he was alive? He would be simply "missing in action." But she would see that the children had a tree, no matter how she felt. A tree? He thought of beautifully decorated trees of Christmases past, and it helped.

On Christmas Eve, and much to their astonishment, they heard the camp radio playing Christmas music in poorest fidelity. No one spoke much, but each man was deep in his own private thoughts of home and family.

The men were roused from their introspection at the sound of the opening of the peep-hatch on the door. Konnie was instantly at the door to receive a small gift which had been donated by the minister of the Evangelical Church of the Democratic Republic of Vietnam.

"Look, fellas!" he exclaimed, almost forgetting to speak in a whisper. "Here's a present for each of us." The men were curious over this act of kindness. "I can't believe it! In this little plastic bag is a tangerine, a cookie and a few pieces of candy. Color! Wow! The bright candy wrappers almost hurt my eyes."

As Jay lay on his pallet that night he wondered why he hadn't given Christmas a little more thought. Surely he could have found some way to bring a little cheer to his buddies.

Christmas morning the camp gong rang as if it were an ordinary day. There had been pleasant dreams of Christmas at home. Hoping to prolong the illusion, the four men slept in. Startled by the familiar bang on the door and the rattle of keys, they scrambled out of bed, knowing the turnkey would be standing at the half-open door in another moment. In his confusion Jay was caught in his mosquito netting. He slipped into one sandal and fumbled around for the other.

"Hey, fellas, I can't find my other sandal," he whispered, agitated.

"Can't find mine either," Konnie whispered back. "Better hurry. He's got the key in the door." The four men struggled to their feet. With one shoe on and one shoe off, Jay and Konnie hurried to join Mike and Gerry who were already at the door.

Then they stopped short in amazement. There, across the room in the half-light of morning, stood a dazzling decorated Christmas tree. Jay and Konnie both shook their heads as if to clear their vision. A Christmas tree! Here? Nobody had entered the room that night. There really was a Santa Claus!

The breathtaking spell was broken by the rasping shout of the guard. After the guard left, Jay and Konnie examined the Christmas tree, probably the most extraordinary one ever erected. In the wonder of that first waking moment, it had contrasted with the dullness of their surroundings and appeared positively brilliant.

Then realization dawned in the half-light. "A broom tree!" Jay whispered. The broom in the room had been set in the teapot, handle down, with the straw wisps upward to simulate branches of the tree. Mike had wound his bandage from his shoulder around the branches like tinsel. Stuck between the wispy straws were the brightly colored candy wrappers from the night before. Scattered beneath the tree were the vivid tangerine peelings and a few fallen leaves. Two rubber-tire sandals were set in front of the tree (Jay and Konnie's missing ones), and two colorfully wrapped pieces of candy had been placed on each sandal. Tears clouded Jay's eyes. It reminded him of seeing shoes filled with goodies at Christmas when he'd been stationed in Germany.

"How did it all get here?" he asked.

"Why — Santa Claus, of course," Mike and Gerry grinned.

Jay and Konnie realized that the men had unselfishly saved those precious pieces of candy from their own gift the night before so they could surprise their buddies with an offering on Christmas morning.

"But where did you get the leaves?" Jay whispered.

"It wasn't easy," Mike said. "We've been trying to save them for weeks, but you kept sweeping them out. We saved them in the well of the window."

Jay chuckled as he recalled sweeping a few strays out almost every day. "I wondered how the rats could carry so many leaves in here! There is a way — even to have Christmas in this place," he whispered. "You fellows were thoughtful enough to make it happen."

Every Christmas Eve from then on the men planned far ahead and fashioned gifts for each other from sheer ingenuity: a needle painstakingly carved from a meat bone in soup; a carved crucifix for a Catholic buddy; a pen shaped from bamboo; ink in a toothpaste cap made from blue iodine balls or cigarette ashes. Later on there were packages, and the prisoners hoarded and concealed items to be used as Christmas gifts for each other. Every Christmas the minister brought a package for each one. There was always a candy exchange, if nothing more.

If anyone had told Jay he must hang on for another five years he might have been tempted to say, "There ain't no way." But through sheer faith and determination there was a way. Jay expresses gratitude to a courageous President; to families who worked to improve their prison treatment; to those who prayed, who wrote letters, who wore POW bracelets; and to those who welcomed them home.

When Jay returned he learned of the mental anguish his family had endured, not knowing if he were dead or alive. Yet they had trimmed a tree every year of his absence and celebrated Christmas, supporting him with their constant faith and prayers.

Last year on his Christmas card to Jay, Gerry penned these words: "Have you seen any broom Christmas trees lately?"

Lt. Col. Jay Hess is retired from the Air Force. He teaches Air Force Junior ROTC at Clearfield High and lives with his wife and children in Bountiful, Utah.

CARMA'S CHRISTMAS

December 1942 was bringing to a close another lean year. We were still suffering the effects of the depression, although fortunately Johnny had a job as laundry supervisor at the new Bushnell Hospital. With the promise of permanent work, we had recently moved to Brigham City.

Little John, age three, and Yolanda, four, were eagerly looking forward to Santa's visit, but they had kept me tied so close to home that I didn't know anyone in town except the landlord. Even though I felt I would die of loneliness, I was too shy to improve my situation.

On Christmas Eve on the way home from work Johnny picked up a tree — they were cheaper that close to Christmas. The children had been put to bed twice already. The fragrant evergreen stood undecorated in front of the living room window of our small house, looking as forlorn as we felt. Neither of us uttered a word, trying not to infect each other with our gloominess.

Little John, in his blue pajamas, wandered into the room, ducking his head from the bright light.

"When's Santa coming?" he asked for the fourth time.

"Now you go back to bed, or he'll never come," Johnny threatened, as he untangled the strings of tree lights.

"Wanta hear the music," Little John insisted in an effort to delay his exit.

"I'll turn it up a little more — but you scoot!" Johnny barely brushed his bottom with a threatening pat. "You don't want to wake Yolanda, do you?"

"Landa not asleep," he said. As if to prove the point, Yolanda, in pink pajamas, appeared in the doorway too.

The glint in her black eyes faded when she saw the naked tree. "Aren't you going to trim the tree? Santa won't find us."

"Back to bed!" I ordered. Johnny seemed to need my reinforcement.

"I want to hear the music," Yolanda also insisted.

"All right, all right. I'd think you'd be tired of that same record."

We had played "White Christmas" at least twenty times. Johnny had brought home an inexpensive portable record player for our Christmas. After the purchase price he had had enough to buy only one record. His selection of "White Christmas" made us even more homesick for our families.

"Now I mean it. To bed!" Johnny ordered.

Little John and Yolanda disappeared into their bedroom at the no-nonsense tone in their father's voice.

Johnny strung the lights on the tree while I unwrapped the ornaments, one by one, from their wrinkled tissue wrappers. By the time I had placed the last ornament on the green branches the whispering and giggling from the bedroom had been replaced by long, even breathing. Little John and Yolanda slept at last.

Johnny brought out a doll for Yolanda — a doll with black hair to match hers. He lifted a little red wagon out of the box ever so gently so it wouldn't rattle and put it under the tree.

I stood on a chair, smoothing the crinkled silver icicles between my fingers and laying them on the branches. Johnny sat in his easy chair, directing me to the sparse spots. The strains of the music droned on for at least the twenty-fifth time: "I'm dreaming of a White Christmas, / Just like the ones I used to know . . ."

"We will have that record worn out the first night," I mused from my perch on the chair.

⁄ Absently I glanced out the window and was suddenly aware that three young soldiers were standing on the sidewalk, staring at me. Feeling extremely self-conscious, I went on straightening the icicles through my fingers. My first impulse was to draw the drapes — but that would be rude. Well, they were rude to stand there and stare at me. They didn't move. They just stood there as if someone had yelled "freeze!" Then the lanky one "unfroze" and rang the doorbell. Johnny unwound from his easy chair and opened the door.

"Please, sir, I know this is out of the ordinary, but could we just step inside and look at your tree? It looks so beautiful from the street."

Johnny cleared his throat. "Of course. Come on in." He opened the door wide and the three stepped into the warmth of the living room. They rubbed their cold hands together and stood awkwardly, breathing in the aroma of the tree.

"Nothing like a Christmas tree," the lanky soldier said. "Looks like a fairy tree. Those icicles remind me of the old legend of the poor family who didn't have anything to put on their tree and during the night the spiders decorated it. Remember?"

We all laughed, a little nervously. Still they stood, simply admiring the tree.

"You fellows stationed at Bushnell Hospital?" Johnny asked.

"Yeah. Medical Corps. You know the restrictions. No tree. No Christmas spirit over there at all," the chubby one ventured. "We're just on our way back from a movie in town. It's tough being away from home at this time of the year."

"Where do you live?" Johnny asked, trying to encourage a conversation.

"Minnesota," the chubby one said. "We always cut our own tree back home."

I thought I detected a brighter glisten in his eyes as he said that last word. He blinked hard. "Hey, look at that black-haired doll. Reminds me of my little sister. Would you believe it? I sent one just like that for her Christmas. Hope she likes it."

"She'll love it," I said, warming up to these homesick boys in uniform. That's all they were — boys!

The eyes of the blond soldier left the star at the top of the tree and traveled down to the foot. "And that little red wagon. Guess you've got a boy and a girl?" He grinned. I nodded. "I haven't seen a red wagon in years. Reminds me of the one I got one Christmas. Mind if I pull it?"

"Of course not," Johnny replied.

The soldier laid the doll in the wagon and pulled it around the living room, chuckling to himself. He was a little boy grown tall.

They briefly chatted of home, then the lanky one said, "We'd better be getting back to the hospital."

"Let me get you a drink of hot, spiced cider. I'm sure you can smell it simmering on the stove," Johnny offered.

"Oh no. We don't want to inconvenience you. We just wanted to see a real live tree in a real live home."

"I insist. It will warm you for the cold walk back to the hospital," Johnny said. "Sit down."

"Oh no — thanks. You've been real nice," the chubby one responded.

"Here — want to help?" I offered, forgetting myself in my interest in them. The lanky one eagerly took a handful of icicles and started to straighten them as he had watched me doing. He could reach the high spots without a chair.

"I don't want to spoil the tree," he said hesitantly.

"You won't. You'll do me a favor — you're so tall," I urged.

Johnny brought in mugs of hot cider. There was more talk of home and past Christmas trees while they sipped their cider and ate fruit cake. Too soon they were saying their good-byes on the porch: "You don't know how much it's meant to us these few moments. Merry Christmas!" Warm smiles wreathed their faces as they trudged on up the street.

Johnny and I sat alone. Suddenly the tree was more dazzling than any we could remember. The music became the most melodious we had ever heard. Each sock hanging from the back of a straight chair bulged with an orange, a banana, hardtack and nuts. What did it matter that there was only a doll and a red wagon under the tree? The children would be delighted. Our hearts were overflowing with gratitude as we enjoyed our quiet hour together, far away from family and friends.

Johnny broke the silence and put words to my own thoughts. "You know, those fellows have changed my whole outlook. We have each other and the kids, and that's the most important. It took those lonely soldiers to bring the Christmas spirit into our home."

This story was told to me by my dear friend Carma Rossi, author of the delightful book Timothy's People.

CHOCOLATE AND VANILLA

Annette and Nancy, ages seven and eight, started off to school hand in hand from their home in Price, a Utah coal town. Since they were only fourteen months apart and inseparable, Mama often dressed them alike. Annette's black ringlets bobbed like springs, and Nancy's golden blond hair was curled all over her pretty head.

"She's chocolate and I'm vanilla," Nancy explained to friends. Annette looked to her big sister as her willing protector. Little did they dream their roles would change. Nancy's ready smile belied her quick temper. If a boy even looked cross-eyed at Annette, she knew Nancy would take care of him in quick order.

After school the two girls returned home, Annette neat and composed as usual, but not so with Nancy. She often returned with her hair disheveled, her socks drooping, her shoes scuffed, and her dress soiled and wrinkled.

Mama sighed. "Nancy, how do you get so dirty?"

Annette was quick in defense. "Johnny teased me, but Nancy got him."

"What a puzzle you are, Nancy," Mama said. "You can't do enough for people. You're always running to the store for a neighbor, or dragging in coal for the old folks in the winter, or delivering flowers in summer. Everyone loves you. But your fists surely make enemies."

"No they don't. Nancy always makes up after," Annette defended.

"They don't hate me," Nancy said. "But they keep their hands off Annette. I have to take care of her — she's my little sister."

In May Annette trudged reluctantly to school without her protector; Nancy had the flu. A few days later Mama pulled the window shades tight because Nancy was covered with red spots and was running an extremely high fever.

The neighbors stopped Annette on her way to school. "How's Nancy?" everyone on the way wanted to know.

"She's real sick," Annette replied one morning to Mrs. Washburn. "Mama says she's got vi-vi-virus me-monia."

"Viral pneumonia?" Mrs. Washburn asked.

"I guess so. That word's too big to say," Annette admitted.

The next day when Mrs. Washburn inquired, Annette reported: "Nancy can't wake up. The doctor says she's in a comma."

"A coma?" Mrs. Washburn asked.

"Uh-huh." Annette's lip trembled, and she hurried on to school, knowing she'd cry if she said more.

The illness developed into post-measle encephalitis. In the hospital Nancy lay on an ice bed, but her fever continued to rage, burning her brain cells. Mama and Daddy took turns staying at the hospital, and Annette felt the lonely days would never end. After twenty-one days Nancy finally emerged from her coma, she was paralyzed from her chest down, unable to speak, and her eyes were crossed.

Mama explained, "The doctor says Nancy must go to the LDS Hospital in Salt Lake."

"But I have to see her first," Annette insisted.

"I'll see what we can do. Nancy misses you too."

The big black hearse, which had been converted to an ambulance, stopped in front of the house. Neighbors gathered instantly. Annette was permitted to climb up to squeeze Nancy's hand for a few brief moments.

"I'm glad you're awake, Nancy. What's wrong with your eyes? You're not looking at me. Look at me!" Annette ordered.

Nancy's eyes filled, but she smiled through her tears.

Mama explained, "Annette, Nancy's eyes can't focus; she's really looking at you, but she can't talk."

"Hurry home. I need you." Annette forced a smile and kissed her sister on the cheek. Then she crawled backward out of the ambulance. Running to Mrs. Washburn, Annette buried her face in her neighbor's skirt and wept bitterly, oblivious to the neighbors who were waving good-bye to Nancy and Mama in the moving ambulance.

By July Nancy was home, able to speak and to see straight. But she couldn't move a muscle of her lower body. Every morning Annette watched Mama rub Nancy for an hour, according to doctor's instructions, and every afternoon Gram came and rubbed her for another hour. By the time school started Nancy was able to sit in a wheelchair, and she started third grade. Annette pushed her to school and anywhere else Nancy wanted to go. It always took a long time to go both ways because Nancy liked to stop and visit with her older friends.

But their roles had changed. Now Annette was Nancy's protector. One day a boy was chanting cruel words. Annette instantly kicked the brake of the wheelchair so Nancy wouldn't roll away, and she raced after the boy. He was so surprised that Annette soon had him on the ground, and the bully was screaming. It was as if Nancy's strength was transferred to her little sister.

Sometimes passersby turned and stared at Nancy. Annette's face reddened. She turned abruptly, glared at them, then stuck out her tongue. One day Nancy looked back and realized what Annette was doing. She reached up and grasped her sister's hand on the chair handle. "Annette, don't do that. That's rude," she chided.

"I can't stand them staring at you. *They* are rude."

"It's all right. They can't help it. I'm strange now — the only one in town in a wheelchair. They don't mean to be rude."

Annette wondered why Nancy was so smart. Perhaps she needed to be, especially now.

As Christmas came around Nancy and Annette talked of gifts. Storybook dolls were the rage that year. How they each wanted one!

Mama warned: "Don't get your hopes up, girls. Santa can't bring much this year. We'll never get Nancy's hospital bills paid."

"It's all right, Mama," Nancy said. "I've got Annette for Christmas. That's all I really want." Annette squeezed her hand.

"I sure missed you while you were gone," Annette assured her. But she had to admit to herself she wanted a storybook doll too, the worst way. Why couldn't she have Nancy *and* a storybook doll?

The day before Christmas Annette kept answering knocks at the door. "Presents are coming one at a time — only it's not Santa Claus. It's all the people we know. Everybody in town has brought you a present, Nancy." Annette kept stacking them up and her eyes grew wide in anticipation.

But with each present Annette's heart was a little heavier. Not one present was for her. In the kitchen she whispered to Mama: "Why are they all for Nancy? Doesn't anybody like me?"

As the tears flowed Mama tried to comfort her. "Annette, of course people like you. It's just that everybody feels sorry for Nancy."

"Don't they feel sorry for me? I don't have a sister to run with any more."

"In a way they're trying to say they're grateful they can walk. And they're trying to pay her back for all the good deeds she did when she could run for them. They miss her sunny smile. You'd do well to be more like Nancy. Even from her bed Nancy spreads a lot of sunshine when people come to visit her. They always go away smiling too. That's a special quality she has."

Mama wiped Annette's tears and hugged her. "Don't let Nancy know you're unhappy. I wish you could have what you want most of all."

But Annette kept her wish locked inside. That would only make Mama feel worse if she knew how much she wanted a storybook doll. "Most of all, I want Nancy to walk," she admitted.

Mama's face grew stern. "Forget it, Annette. She never will."

Annette grabbed the coal bucket and ran out to fill it, hoping that the cold would take the redness from her eyes so Nancy wouldn't know she'd been crying.

On Christmas morning Annette was excited to see what was in Nancy's packages. Only once did Annette hurt inside because she had received only the necessary clothes and no storybook doll.

"Annette, you help me unwrap all these presents," Nancy announced. The girls stretched the gift opening. They giggled and oohed and aahed over each gift: games, books, puzzles, coloring books, crayons, all sorts of therapeutic hand toys, and dolls, dolls, dolls! They had never seen so many storybook dolls all at once, even in the store: George Washington, Martha Washington, Betsy Ross, foreign dolls, and, of all things, two breathtaking bride dolls, one with black hair and the other with golden blond hair.

"Count them all, Annette," Nancy ordered. "How many presents are there?"

Annette counted: "Fifty-one . . . ninety-four, ninety-five, ninety-six . . . one hundred and one! Oh, Nancy, you're so lucky!" Then she caught herself and wished she could cut out her tongue. She glanced at Nancy's immobile legs and then at her own, but the smile never left Nancy's face.

"You bet I'm lucky. Put the gifts in two stacks, Annette. You get half of them — fifty. But most of all, I want you to choose the one present you would like more than anything else. It's yours! That gives you fifty-one."

Almost reluctantly Annette reached out and took the black-haired bride doll in her exquisite white dress. "Could I have this?"

"I hoped you'd take it, it matches your black hair. And we can play brides because I have one with golden blond hair. They're chocolate and vanilla — like us. Oh, this is the best Christmas in the whole world — not just for the presents — but because I'm home, not in the hospital, and because people love me."

Nancy and Annette grew up to be unusually attractive girls. Both are loved by all who know them. About a year after having the measles, Nancy's golden blond hair began to fade to brown;

the girls are no longer chocolate and vanilla. Nancy spent subsequent years in and out of hospitals. Her bones were so fragile that they broke without the slightest injury. When she was nineteen her legs were amputated almost to the hips. But she has never lost her magnetic smile and personality. She is married to another amputee, and they are one of the happiest couples in the world. They maintain their own home and are independent citizens.

Annette has always been Nancy's protector and the close bond of love between them grows with the years. Brown-haired Nancy sat in her wheelchair as matron of honor during a lengthy reception when Annette became my black-haired daughter-in-law. Two beautiful "dolls" played bride in real life.

ROUND-ROBIN CHRISTMAS

The telephone jangled like Christmas bells.

Marge, the voice on the other end, was excited. "Dora, I've just got to tell you about the project my girls are doing for Christmas."

"Go ahead, Marge." Her enthusiasm was always contagious.

"You know my Mia Maids at church? Well, I decided it's time the girls learned about giving. They've gone along with giving anonymously. That was all right. But listen to this test. This year they won't even know whom they're giving to."

"Isn't it enough to learn to give without being thanked?" I asked.

"Oh no," Marge hurried on. "I've decided on the grandest couple. He's on rather skimpy retirement and has some health problems. The girls asked if I would let them in on the secret after Christmas, but I told them that would spoil everything. These people must *never* know where the fruit basket came from. I'll slip in some money too. You can't trace green money. Won't that be fun? After the girls thought about it they caught the excitement too. I'll let you know how it works out. Bye now."

Two days later my friend Alice was on the phone. "Dora, I've had the strangest thing happen. This morning my neighbor on the corner delivered a big red basket of fruit. It's beautiful, but there's no name on it. My neighbor said that a woman rang her doorbell and asked if Alice Markham lived around here.

" 'Just up the street,' my neighbor said.

"The woman asked, 'Would you see that she gets this basket?' My neighbor had never seen her before. So she brought it over. But ten dollars was inside an envelope on top of the fruit," she admitted hesitantly.

"Isn't that great? Pin money before Christmas," I replied.

"But I can't use this money without knowing whom to thank."

"Oh come on, Alice, haven't you ever had a secret pal?"

"No. Look, I simply can't use this. It isn't right."

"It isn't right if you don't. Surely you've heard about all the Brownie points people want to chalk up at Christmas. I've heard of others who have found goodies on their doorsteps this year. Anonymity is in vogue."

"But not money. I simply can't spend it with a clear conscience."

"Look, be glad for someone's generosity and use it gratefully."

"The fruit would have been plenty." Then she continued after a long pause: "You know, it's real strange — almost weird. Yesterday after my daughter got off work she took me to the craft store. They had ten dollars for me, my profit from my projects they'd sold. Then we picked up her little boy and his babysitter, and took the sitter home. On the way I asked the sitter what she wanted for Christmas. She said: 'Not much — and I probably won't get much either. But if I don't get some new clothes, anything at all, I can't go back to school after New Year's.'

"Then as she slipped out of the car in front of her house I put the ten dollars I had just received in her hand and said, 'Merry Christmas.' She objected, but I insisted she keep it."

"See, Alice?" I said. "You really couldn't spare that ten dollars. You probably need it more than she does, but you gave it unselfishly, and it came back to you via some other generous soul. Of course you'll use it. How would you feel if that babysitter didn't buy something new for school with your money?"

"I hadn't thought of it that way. Now I can get Jim the new shirt he needs."

Now it was my turn to call Marge. "Marge, I know who received your fruit basket."

"Oh no. That spoils it," she said.

"I promise never to tell her. But she did get it all right."

"How do you know?"

"She called me."

"How do you know it was the same person? Was there anything else with it?"

"An envelope with ten dollars."

"Then she got it intact." Marge was relieved.

"She can't use the money."

"Why not?"

"Not without knowing whom to thank."

"Oh no! Did you convince her?"

"Yes." Then I told Marge how Alice had given her own ten dollars to the babysitter.

"How about that? I really debated about putting that money in. I didn't want to hurt anyone's pride. And giving money is touchy. I took it out, then at the last minute I stuffed it in again, and I guess the prompting was right. You know, Dora, this is the beginning of a new tradition we'll carry out as a family. Every year we'll see that someone's life is enriched because we give of ourselves anonymously, not taking or expecting credit, and no one can feel indebted to us to try to pay us back. Isn't that what Christmas is all about?"

GIFT EXCHANGE

Douglas sat at the table in the university library in Berkeley, head in hands, not even seeing the formulas in organic chemistry which were outlined in the book before him. Instead his thoughts were on Luella and their two little girls, Helen and Phyllis. He thought, I wish Christmas didn't come this year. I hardly have a penny to my name. My nose is so buried in books from all my cramming that I haven't had a minute to make anything with my hands. And if Father's check doesn't come today we won't even have enough to buy the makings of Christmas dinner.

He dug into his pocket and counted the coins in his purse. His scholarship fund left nothing for living after paying school expenses. Yet he was unable to work, since all his time and attention must be utilized in preparing himself to qualify for the doctoral program, and Luella couldn't work because of the babies. The year was 1926, and there were no day-care centers. The couple were dependent on supplementary funds from his parents.

"I feel like throwing it all over," Douglas muttered. "But I have a responsibility to my parents when they're so insistent on helping me." He slammed his books shut and headed home to their small apartment.

As he opened the door, Luella put her fingers to her lips. "Shhh — the girls are napping, and I'm so anxious to finish these for tomorrow." She displayed two stuffed dressed dolls which she had made from scraps. "And they didn't cost a thing," she whispered, smiling with self-satisfaction.

"Dangit! I'm a sorry failure. You have to do it all!"

"Why, Douglas, I didn't mean to hurt you. I should certainly hold up my end when you're strained to the limit. I'm sorry." Her voice was edgy.

"*I'm* sorry. Forgive me. Has the mail come?"

"Yes. But the check didn't."

"What now? The bank account is all but overdrawn. And I don't have a gift for you. You can't imagine how that makes me feel."

"Well, if it's any comfort to you, I don't have one for you either. After all, we're adults and as long as the little girls have something . . . They'll love these dolls."

"Honey, what would you do if I gave you five dollars for a Christmas gift?"

For a moment Luella was pensive, then her face broke into a warm smile. "Why, I'd make it my present to you."

He kissed her on the cheek and the resentment inside melted. "But what will we have for Christmas dinner?" Douglas asked.

"Old Mother Hubbard went to her cupboard . . ."

"Don't tell me — it's bare."

"Well, it will be a first for Christmas dinner, but I guess we can always have bread and milk and be grateful. At least I can make fresh bread."

Douglas absently fumbled through his books on the table. "Dumb me, Luella, I've got to go back to the library. I brought a wrong book. I'll be right back and then I'll help you clean up the apartment so it will look nice, even if we don't have a tree and decorations."

In his mind he was groping for ideas. Bread and milk for Christmas dinner? At the library he could make a telephone call from a pay phone. Back at the library he found the right book. He fumbled in his pocket for his last dime and went to the telephone booth. The cheery voice of Dr. MacDonald answered, and Douglas could almost see the smiling, ruddy face of the professor.

"Dr. MacDonald," he hesitated and cleared his throat, then forced himself to speak up. "Is there something I could do to help you — perhaps some work? Luella and I couldn't afford to go home for Christmas and — I'm desperate."

Dr. MacDonald cut in. "Yes, there is something you could do for me. Could you and your family come and share Christmas dinner with us tomorrow?"

"You mean it? What time?"

Douglas fairly sprinted back to the apartment. How relieved Luella would be! Just thinking of her turned on a light in his brain.

Christmas morning as Helen and Phyllis hugged their dolls Douglas handed Luella an envelope. Her face flushed.

"But Douglas, I haven't anything for you. I told you . . ."

"Open it."

From the envelope Luella took a check signed by Douglas made out to her for one hundred dollars.

"Oh, Honey, how generous of you," she said. "Well, I guess I do have a gift for you after all." She picked up his pen and endorsed the check, returned it to the envelope, and handed it back to her husband.

"Thank you for not trying to cash it," he smiled. "I guess we do have a gift — our love for each other — and it doesn't cost a cent."

Dr. C. Douglas Barnes was a research supervisor for Union Oil Company for many years and later taught at Long Beach City College.

UNEXPECTED CONTRIBUTION

My brother John has been an enterpriser and showman from Day One. We had a player piano which compensated for our lack of skill at the keyboard. The piano stood proudly in the living room in such a position that anyone sitting on the porch could look through the window and see the pianist. Frequently John, who was slightly older than most of the neighborhood kids, would close the small sliding doors over the player rolls and pretend to perform the most complicated pieces with all the flourishes of an artist. Because of the folds of the sheer curtains, he could maintain his hoax.

His audience regarded him as a born musician, but found him too "humble" to play for them when they came into the house. Consequently they would line the bench on the porch and listen to him "practice." He could even change the rolls unobtrusively, since the curtain blurred his movements. During those roll changes they thought he was simply finding new numbers in the books which he kept open on the music rack before him.

As Christmas rolled around when John was about twelve, he hit upon a money-making idea. He organized the best singers among his young friends and taught them many carols. One of the girls offered to accompany with her violin. John was delighted. This would insure a more professional performance.

On a snowy twentieth of December the whole group followed their pied piper up Second Avenue past the familiar houses to a more affluent neighborhood where they were not known. They stopped at several large houses, ablaze with lights. After singing two or three carols, at John's suggestion, the group moved on up the street. In his most businesslike manner he strode up to the house where they had just sung and rang the doorbell. When the owner answered (usually the man of the house) John announced, "We're caroling for the Salvation Army." Invariably the residents gave him money.

The evening wore on until the kids were too cold to sing any more, and they all hurried home. John didn't even notice the cold because of the wealth jingling in his pocket.

The next afternoon after school John hurried to his bedroom and closed the door to count his loot. Of course, it would have to be divided between the participants. He thought to himself, Mom said I could go downtown today to finish my shopping. I'll take my share and then tonight I can divvy up the other kids' shares.

The stacks of coins added up to far more than he had expected. Then his conscience spoke up: "You can't spend that money for what you want. You collected it in the name of the Salvation Army. Nobody would have given you money if you had told them the truth — that you wanted it for your own private charity."

He divided the stacks into equal amounts for each singer. His conscience kept prodding. Then he pulled out his gift list from the drawer. He had only two presents left to buy, one for Mom and one for Dad. His share would buy a big bottle of cologne for Mom and a classy blue tie to go with Dad's Sunday suit.

Conscience interrupted his figuring. "That money should go to the Salvation Army like I told you. You've still got time to make a wooden trivet for the dinner table in shop class for your mother. And you could give your dad an IOU for shoveling the walks the rest of the winter. Come on, now. Be honest with yourself. Your parents wouldn't want gifts you bought with money collected for charity."

John sighed. "Okay, you win."

He put one heavy paper sack inside another for strength, then hastily scooped in all the coins before he had a chance to change his mind.

"I hope I can convince the other kids this is the only way to go," he said aloud. He slipped into his warm coat and pulled his cap down over his ears. "Be back soon, Mom," he called as he hurried out the front door.

The bus ride to town took only a few minutes. On the bank corner he spotted a Salvation Army Santa Claus ringing his bell beside his pot suspended from a tripod. With only a moment's hesitation he walked deliberately up to the pot and opened his paper sack. To himself he thought, I might as well enjoy every bit of this. The bearded man in the red suit stopped ringing his bell in amazement as he watched John drop the half-dollars, quarters, dimes and nickels into the pot one at a time.

"Merry Christmas, young man. God bless you for your generosity."

"Thanks, I'll need that when I explain to my friends," John said, as he left Santa scratching his head at the weighty contribution of a boy so young.

Today my brother John is a vice president at the Wells Fargo Bank and Trust in Los Angeles, California.